Also by Marguerite Vance

HEAR THE DISTANT APPLAUSE!
Six Great Ladies of the American Theatre

COURAGE AT SEA

SCOTLAND'S QUEEN:
The Story of Mary Stuart

A FLOWER FROM DINAH

DARK EMINENCE:
Catherine de Medici and her Children

THE WORLD FOR JASON

THE LAMP LIGHTERS:
Women in the Hall of Fame

JEPTHA AND THE NEW PEOPLE

ASHES OF EMPIRE:
Carlota and Maximilian of Mexico

WILLIE JOE AND HIS SMALL CHANGE

SONG FOR A LUTE

LEAVE IT TO LINDA

FLIGHT OF THE WILDLING:
Elisabeth of Austria

SECRET FOR A STAR

THE EMPRESS JOSEPHINE:
From Martinique to Malmaison

WINDOWS FOR ROSEMARY

THE BOY ON THE ROAD

ELIZABETH TUDOR:
Sovereign Lady

THE JACKSONS OF TENNESSEE

LADY JANE GREY:
Reluctant Queen

MARIE ANTOINETTE:
Daughter of an Empress

THE LEES OF ARLINGTON

PATSY JEFFERSON OF MONTICELLO

MARTHA:
Daughter of Virginia

WHILE SHEPHERDS WATCHED

A STAR FOR HANSI

Esther Wheelwright
INDIAN CAPTIVE

Esther Wheelwright
INDIAN CAPTIVE

by Marguerite Vance

illustrated by Lorence F. Bjorklund

E. P. Dutton & Co., Inc.   New York

First Printing   April 1964
Second Printing September 1964
Third Printing   November 1965

Published simultaneously in Canada by Clarke,
Irwin & Company Limited, Toronto and Vancouver

Library of Congress Catalog Card Number: 64-13918

For
Elizabeth and Suzanne Ochoa

Esther Wheelwright
INDIAN CAPTIVE

1

THAT August morning in 1703 was very still — still as though time were holding its breath, waiting for something. Bees tumbled about in the clover, grasshoppers polished their wings as they clung along the tall grass and day-lily stems, and from the shadows of the pine woods bordering the meadow on the west a mourning dove made its gentle complaint. Otherwise silence lay over the land.

Little Esther Wheelwright looked younger than her six years. She was pink-cheeked and freckled and dimples played in each cheek as she smiled in satisfaction at the firkin she was busily filling with blueberries. There would be pudding for supper. Mama had promised. Perhaps she'd better go home — the firkin was almost full. She squinted at the sun. Yes, it was time. For a moment she looked ruefully at the stains on the neat pinafore buttoned over her linsey-woolsey. She had promised to be careful but berries had a way of rolling and smashing when you tried to catch them. Mama wouldn't scold, though. She almost never did.

Esther could hear her brothers whooping and shouting in the big barn. Mathew, thirteen, was the great tease. It was Mathew who loved to tell the frightening Indian stories, ending each one with a blood chilling shriek and the threat, "You be a good girl, Esther, or I'll tell the Indians, and whoop, whoop, whoop, they'll scalp you just like that!"

Mathew could remember the Abenaki raid seven years earlier and though the memory of it still haunted him, filling him with terror, he could not resist teasing his youngest sister with it. She teased so beautifully, anticipating the end of each story even before it was reached, running, screaming, while he came after her, swinging an imaginary war club, catching her eventually, to hold her wriggling, screaming with laughter while he blew on her neck. It was a glorious, scary game because, of course, there was nothing to be frightened of. The Indians were gone — none had been seen in years. Esther had only Mathew's lurid description to help her guess what they looked like.

"Come, Major," she called, and watched the little spaniel bounding toward her through the long grass. "Come, Maj — —" Like the lash of a whip a steely arm encircled her neck and a hand clamped down over her mouth. She was borne to her knees, then lifted, pulled up and back against a brown chest.

Indians! Without quite knowing how she realized this, the

thought struck her with such sickening force that it was like a physical blow. This was not Mathew in a teasing mood; this was quite different, so bewildering and terrifying that she felt sick at her stomach from sheer fright, and her body went limp. By a frantic effort she did for a second manage to push the hand from her mouth.

"Mama!" she screamed. "Mama, come help me!"

Then something struck her from behind and she crumpled. When she woke she was still being carried against the brown chest that smelled of sweat and bear grease. Feebly she began to kick.

"I want my mama," she wept. "Put me down! I want to go home!"

After seven years the Abenakis were back.

War had again broken out between France and England in 1702. This war was known in America as Queen Anne's War and in Europe as the War of the Spanish Succession. These wars, which scarred Canada and New England so cruelly, had begun in the seventeenth century when France and England both grasped for great tracts of territory in the New World. The region which extended from the Gulf of the St. Lawrence south into Maine was called Acadia and was claimed by both the French and English. The French feared that the English would gain control of Acadia and would cut them off from the rich fur country to the west.

More and more English were moving into the territory,

building homesteads and laying out farms. Acadia was becoming English. Now the indignation of the French and the fury of the Indians combined. The English defended their homes, and, as in all wars, there were torture and death on both sides and the English families in Maine suffered terribly.

From one of these families was Esther Wheelwright. Her father, John Wheelwright, was a man who owned much of the little village of Wells on the southern tip of Maine. Its gristmill and its sawmill and much of its rich farm land were his. It was John Wheelwright who had acted as commander of the little Wells garrison at the time of the Indian massacre in 1696. His name was known among the Abenakis and the capture of his daughter was a triumph. She would bring a handsome price as a prisoner of war. Far better this than a ransom demanded of her father with the risk of capture and punishment, possibly death. Esther was a real prize.

The forest was dusky and the moccasins of the raiding party made no sound on the pine needles. By lifting her head ever so slightly Esther could peer up into the painted face above her. Streaks of scarlet and ocher covered the lean cheeks; the eyes were outlined in white, and black and white lines stretched from the outside corners of the eyes and the jaw. It made a fearsome sight and the little girl sobbed in terror.

Then her captor set her on the ground and took her hand. Deeper, ever deeper into the forest they went. The terrain changed. Widely spaced pine and spruce trees gave way to thick undergrowth which whipped viciously about Esther's face as she scrambled along as best she could. She tried not to cry but she was tired and frightened. Tears ran unheeded down her cheeks, dripping from her chin to the starched yoke of her pinafore. Blinded, she rubbed her eyes on the hem that smelled of soap and water and home, wondering as she did why suddenly they seemed to be hurrying so. She looked up over the edge of her pinafore.

They were entering a clearing. Five wigwams formed a semicircle, the open end of which faced the approaching party, and in its center fires burned under two great cooking pots tended by two Indian women. One was old and fat and lumpish, with long wisps of gray hair that dangled limply over the steaming pot she was stirring. The other woman was younger and when she looked up her eyes were like shining chestnuts.

In her wretchedness Esther had not realized that others had joined the party. Now she became aware of two more Indians in war regalia leading two boys about Mathew's age and an old man leaning on a cane, his face gray with weariness. The younger woman came forward and said something to Esther's captor. He answered abruptly, waving his arm in a wide circle to the right, and then followed the other two Indians and their captives out of sight into the gathering shadows. Esther could not know it, but he had explained that other members of the large raiding party, of which this was only a part, had gone farther west. It was a strategy of the Indians to split up their parties, converging later at some prearranged spot farther to the north inside the Canadian border.

The woman took Esther's hand, stopping only for a final glimpse at the bubbling pot, and led her into a wigwam.

"Please." Almost too tired to stand, the little girl made one more effort. Perhaps this woman would understand how she felt and help her. "Won't you please take me home? *Please* let me go to my mama! Please!"

Her face smarted cruelly from the lashing it had taken from the underbrush. Her lip was bleeding and a deep scratch across her cheek throbbed. Mama would have bathed it with warm water and rubbed on wolfsbane; and the thought brought fresh tears.

The woman chose to ignore them. Instead, she turned Esther firmly toward her and, pointing to herself, repeated several times, "Didias — Didias — Didias." She was telling Esther her name and Esther understood and answered quickly, "Esther Wheelwright — Esther — I am Esther."

Didias smiled faintly. "Esther," she said and put her hand on the girl's shoulder, "Esther — Didias."

But Esther pulled away from her and began screaming, "I don't want you. I want my mother." A firm hand was clamped quickly over her mouth until she stopped.

Evening had come and from the wigwams the Indian men and women came to gather around the cooking pots. Esther found there were no girls of her age in the camp; the other

children were babies. Seated on the ground between Didias and the old woman, she obediently dipped the *emkwan*, a large wooden spoon, into the stew and lifted out a morsel of food. Then, shuddering, she put it back. It was some small ground animal — field mouse, young mole or chipmunk — and the thought of eating it turned her sick. She noticed that the Indians ate their helpings like bread, biting, chewing, biting, chewing until the morsel was consumed. There seemed to be no fussy nibbling around bones, though these were somehow discarded, but just a silent, methodical chewing and swallowing. Through a haze of weariness Esther looked on silently, fascinated, but she could not eat.

The Indians laughed and the old woman tried to force a tidbit on her. But Esther hid her face against Didias's arm, and though the woman drew away and cuffed her good-naturedly, she got up and took her back into the wigwam.

In the wigwam, Didias began rummaging among a pile of skins. She held up something faintly resembling a child's coat. It was made of buckskin, dark and stiff, and smelled like spoiled venison. The wigwam was filled with the same horrid odor. The Abenakis took pride in their curing of skins and the articles of clothing they made from them. However, the garment Esther looked at must have been a failure, worked by some very young and inexperienced girl, for its texture was harsh and it had little shape.

Didias held it up to her, smiling, and began quickly to unfasten Esther's pinafore and dress. As they dropped to the ground the new costume was slipped over her head and her own clothes were tossed aside. Too tired to think clearly, Esther stood first on one foot, then on the other, balancing herself against Didias's shoulder while the Indian woman took off her sturdy shoes and stockings. These she replaced with a pair of women's legging-moccasins, much too large, which she tied on with thongs of hide. Then she pushed Esther down on the pile of skins and covered her with them. She left the wigwam, and the little girl fell into a deep sleep. Her last waking thought was of Major bounding through the high grass and of Mama expecting her home with blueberries for pudding.

When Esther woke she saw, a few inches away, the old woman lying on her back, snoring. Through the open door-way, she could see the gray dawn blotting out the stars. Birds twittered and trilled and somewhere a dog barked a deep, bugle-like greeting to the day.

Her first thought was, Where am I? Then the terrors of the day before came back to her. She sat up, feeling unclean, tasting on her lips the acrid smoke that filled the wigwam, her eyes smarting, her chest and shoulders a-prickle under the stiff skin of her dress. The early morning air was cold, and when she stood up she felt as if she were standing naked in a large empty box which offered neither warmth nor comfort.

Didias handed her a morsel of food on a stick and, because she was faint with hunger, she ate it while she listened and tried to understand the Indian woman's monologue and pan-tomime. Soon she realized they were breaking camp and that she would be supposed to carry her share of the equipment.

Didias rolled the pile of skins in their tent into a bundle and tied it with thongs of hide. She placed a *tumpline* across Esther's forehead and fastened the ends of the strap to the bundle, which she placed on her back. She patted Esther on the shoulder encouragingly. Esther found the load was heavy but not more than she could manage and she walked a few paces to test her strength.

The brave who had captured her the day before — it seemed a year — waved in her direction and spoke to another Indian who, with two Indian women, was busily taking down the wigwams. They worked silently, and Esther's captor when he passed her, thumped her shoulder in amiable fashion.

His name was Sabbatis, and with his paint removed he was not quite so fearsome looking. He seemed to be the leader of the band, and now he gave orders and moved off in a northerly direction, the camp following. Esther, between the old woman and Didias, trudged forward under her heavy load. Her first day as a member of the Abenaki tribes had begun.

2

NORTH and ever north they traveled, up the Kennebec River. The drowsy haze of September lay over the land. The days were hot, the nights cold, and here and there a maple showed a sudden golden flame of color. After weeks of following the trails through the unbroken forest they came to a halt. Here, by prearrangement they were joined by the other Abenakis from whom they had separated after the attack on Wells.

When the two parties joined Esther spied among the Indians a familiar face. It was Titus Jones. Titus was a Negro boy, one of the most trustworthy of her father's slaves. The entire family loved Titus. When he looked up wearily, hopelessly, as the party halted and saw Esther standing among the clutter and debris of the camp, it was more than he could bear. He buried his face in his hands and sobs shook his slight body.

Esther ran to him, arms outstretched. "Titus. Oh Titus, where are they — the others? Mama? And Papa and my brothers and sisters? How did you get here? Where are we going?"

"I don't know, Miss Esther." Titus's voice was muffled and he rubbed his sleeve across his eyes. "Everything happened so fast. I —— " A brave caught him by the arm and spun him around and, pushing him before him, disappeared into the forest. Esther never saw Titus again.

Her first agonizing homesickness and longing for her family gradually lessened as the weeks passed. The Wheelwrights were a deeply religious Puritan family and Esther never missed saying her nightly prayers. Now, among strangers, she found them wonderfully comforting. God as a loving Father became real as He never had been before. Sometimes, bent double under her load as she followed Didias along the trails, she sang what she had always thought of as her "happy song," a little song the Wheelwright children all had sung from babyhood:

> God takes care of me,
> Care of me, care of me,
> So shall I happy be
> All the day long.
>
> No harm can come to me,
> Come to me, come to me,
> Who holds my hand but He
> All the day long?

Esther had made a marching song of it, her sunburned little face lifted to the skies as she sang. She was not reprimanded;

she was well treated; and but for a shadow of loneliness she might have been almost happy.

The two reunited bands, after another few weeks of steady trudging through the wilderness, reached the main encampment consisting of several hundred Indians. The new arrivals added their wigwams to the village, already set up in orderly formation, each dwelling facing east. The wigwams, built of logs and birch bark, were sturdy and roomy and cozy, though always hazy with smoke from the fire burning continuously in the center of each.

Girls and boys romped and raced through the spaces between dwellings, playing games Esther could not understand or follow. One day she took courage and approached a group of girls playing a game using sticks with which they tried to strike one another's ankles.

They did not resent her interference with their game but for a moment they stood, startled, looking at her with grave, unblinking interest. Esther now knew a few Abenaki words and, with gestures to help her, she managed to string together a sentence which the girls seemed to understand.

"Look — go so," she invited as she took the hands of two girls and indicated that they take the hands of two others, and so finally form a circle. One of the older girls, Matoaka, seemed to understand at once and began slowly to walk to the right, starting the circle turning, shouting as she did, "Good! Good! Esther knows a new game."

So a friendship was struck between the two girls and Es-

24

ther's eyes were sparkling as she slowly began singing a chant her mother must have known as a child:

> A tisket, a tasket,
> A green and yellow basket,
> I sent a letter to my love
> And on the way I dropped it,
> Dropped it — dropped it.
> I dropped it once, I dropped it twice
> I dropped it three times over —
> Over — over.

As she sang she walked in the opposite direction from that taken by the moving circle, waving a small branch of hemlock as she walked. At the last word, "over," she dropped the branch behind the girl she was passing. The girl would pick it up and chase her around the circle while she tried to reach the vacant place before she could be caught. If caught, she must repeat the song again. If she was not caught, the other girl took her place.

"More, Esther, more! Tisket-tasket, Esther!" Laughing and hopping about in excitement, the Indian girls pressed about their new English friend as she taught them the words of the old song game.

"It's easy," she assured them when they stumbled at "three times over," and Matoaka, beaming, volunteered proudly, "I'll teach, too. Tisket-tasket is a good game. Maybe Esther knows more?"

Yes, Esther assured them, she did know more, but Didias had work for her to do and the games must wait. Her lap filled with skins which Didias had cut, she stitched together the simple *manude*, a small bag made of woodchuck hide, or she braided grass for baskets. As her fingers grew more skilled, she learned to make the narrow grass headbands so popular with the women. Though Didias seldom praised her, Esther knew when she was pleased for quite unconsciously she would break into a little song that sounded like a lullaby, singing it under her breath: *He'-hai-gwa'-ni-ho'-yu-wa-ni'.* Esther loved to listen to the long-drawn-out syllables, repeated over and over again until she, too, could sing them.

Sometimes laughter drifted from Sabbatis's wigwam where he played *kwakwanigan,* a kind of checkers, with one of his cronies. And sometimes from some part of the camp which Esther could not find, there came the deep, bugle-like barking of a dog. Once she asked Didias about it.

"He must be a very big dog," she added, "because his bark is so loud and he . . ."

But Didias held up her hand in an anxious gesture meaning, "Stop! Do not speak of it any more," and Esther tried to put it out of her mind. She did not succeed, however, for she loved dogs, and the more she thought of it the deeper became her interest and her curiosity.

There were corn meal, maize, dried berries, fish and game on hand and the camp seemed well off. Then winter came, a winter of such storms as no tribesman could recall. Supplies dwindled and in many wigwams the fire went out and songs of mourning rose above the screaming wind. Then the evil sickness, smallpox, swept down on the camp like a great black bird, and no one was spared. The old squaw was the first to die, then Matoaka and her whole family, and on a bitter night Didias rose in her delirium and disappeared into the storm and did not come back.

Esther was alone, too sick to move or to realize in what danger she was: a sick captive child, a nuisance and a hindrance, was often put to death to lighten the burden of the camp. But so little strength remained in any creature in that wretched camp that she was ignored and forgotten. However, Esther managed to survive the filth, the fever, and the burning, itching sores covering her body. Nor was she scarred.

When finally spring broke through, the remaining remnants of the Abenaki band, believing their camp site was haunted by evil spirits, moved on. They settled near Norwidgewock not far from Skowhegan on the Kennebec. Here Esther, with a bag of corn seed slung over her shoulder, was out with the other girls and women planting the season's crops. The Abenakis were never farming people but each spring out of necessity they planted corn and beans.

Esther was now almost eight. She was sturdy and cheerful, adapting her little "happy tune" to planting, weeding, and any other task that came to hand. She fitted into the pattern of Indian life without complaining. Many of the Indian children she had known had been taken by the smallpox and now she saw little of those who remained, but spent much of her time with the women or, when not working, wandered alone by the river. She was not watched, so contented she seemed. Time passed; memory faded; the past was an uncertain dream. Esther submitted quietly to having her fair hair darkened with bear grease and soot, and her body rubbed with it. Her disguise was perfect. Only an astute searcher could have seen Esther Wheelwright unless, of course, he had looked into her blue eyes. Gradually she became an Indian.

On a summer morning she had taken her grass and quills for weaving to a favorite spot remote from the camp on a little pebbly beach beside the river. She hummed softly as she worked. The forest was still except for a bad-tempered blue jay shrieking and scolding as it flew over her retreat on the riverbank.

"Oh, keep still!" she called. "Nobody's going to hurt you and you make such a terrible noise!"

As she looked up to follow its flight her eye caught a movement in the underbrush and she put down her work, trying not to be frightened. There it was again, a slow, exploring movement, hostile and unfriendly. Esther found her hands shaking. Then the bushes parted and an enormous dog stepped cautiously toward her. It was a finely bred mastiff, smoke-colored, blunt-nosed. In spite of its great size, it was pitifully thin, ribs showing plainly through the satiny gray coat. Stiff-legged, as though stalking prey, hackles rising along its back, lips drawn back in a menacing snarl, the big animal moved slowly toward Esther.

Oddly enough the moment Esther recognized that the intruder was a dog, her fear left her and with a smile of relief she scrambled to her feet. The dog growled menacingly, then stopped as though deciding whether or not to spring. Fearlessly, happily, Esther walked toward it, a small hand held out in welcome.

"Come, pretty boy," she greeted it. "Come — don't be afraid and don't look so cross. I am just Esther. We'll be friends. I'll call you — what shall I call you — Major, maybe?"

From her pocket she took a flat wafer of pemmican, which was to have been her lunch, and held it out to the mastiff. The dog sniffed, took another step forward, and now its tail began to swing, slowly, contentedly. Esther reached out and stroked the great head. "Come — eat — it is good."

Eagerly the big dog snapped up the dried meat and deep in its throat the growl turned to a whine of satisfaction. It looked at Esther with friendly amber eyes now, tail swinging, and rubbed its head against her. She dropped to her knees, threw her arms about the powerful neck, and laid her cheek against the big head. Her fingers moving across the dog's throat encountered something which at first she did not

29

recognize, so deeply was it imbedded in the flesh, then she realized she was touching a strand of rope.

"Hold still," she admonished. Finding the knot was not easy and untying it was harder still. The dog stood perfectly still after a first nervous straining to relieve the added torture of Esther's tugging to untie the knot. When at last the choking rope fell, the dog shook itself again and again and then threw itself on the ground, rolling in an ecstasy of relief and Esther hovered over it, crooning her sympathy. "Poor old fellow," she murmured, busy fingers rubbing the chafed throat, "whoever did that to you was wicked. Never mind, we'll go to the village and put salve on it, then you'll feel better."

The dog seemed to agree for it pranced a little and barked, a dog's laughing, affectionate bark. Esther found herself laughing, too, in sheer happiness for her new friend. "Now I'll always know it's you when I hear you bark in the night," she told him, "or maybe Sabbatis will let you come and live in my wigwam. Didias would have, I know."

But Didias was not there. Someone else was, however. Like an unexpected hurricane, a young brave came crashing through the bushes, anger making his face a very storm cloud of wrath. When he saw the dog he came to a sliding stop and pointed, grinning maliciously, and "Major" stiffened.

"So," the Indian said, "Esther tried to escape and the dog caught her! Now you come with me to Sabbatis! The English girl is not so smart. Come along!"

He caught her by the shoulder, but she twisted away and the dog growled. "That's not true!" her voice shook with

anger at the unjust charge. "I came here — I do almost every day — to weave. The dog came and we were playing. He is my friend. He was almost choked with a rope. I took it off because it hurt him. He had torn it too."

"You are lying! Come now to Sabbatis and be flogged."

The brave took her arm. The dog began to growl menacingly. Esther pulled away and went over to the dog. She spoke to it in a low voice, and gently patted its head. "Never you mind, Major, Sabbatis will not hurt us." Then the Indian led her back to the camp, the dog at her heels. Sabbatis, in council with three of his braves in his wigwam, looked up in astonishment at the trio that appeared suddenly in the doorway. A half-smile played about his lips as he spied Esther, then as the dog edged forward, pressing against her skirts, and the young Indian brushed past them, shouting his accusation, the Chief's expression changed.

"Esther, you speak first. Never have you lied to us. Now tell us how this came to pass. Then Black Fox shall speak. And you, Black Fox, how many times have I told you not to enter my councils without first asking my permission? Speak, Esther."

And Esther spoke freely but without rancor. Her cheeks were flaming under their coating of grease and her eyes were dark. "Let me have the dog, O Chief," she said. It was clear that she was not interested in Black Fox's charge. Her whole thought was for the dog. "He was so hurt. Let me have him. With him I would be safe anywhere. I did not run away. Why would I sit and weave if I wanted to leave my friends? But please, *please* may I have the dog for my own?"

Sabbatis nodded. "The dog is a good hunter of captives who would escape, but if he is to stay a good hunter then he must have some care. Though he is of little worth otherwise, he must not be abused." He called the dog to him and ran his finger around its sore neck. "He shall be yours, Esther. Now go back to your weaving. Black Fox, you will come here when my council is ended."

Esther longed to put into words all the gratitude she felt, but faced by the stern Chief with his unblinking black eyes and grim, thin-lipped mouth, she faltered. "Thank you, O Chief," was all she could manage, before she left the wigwam, the great dog at her heels. Black Fox disappeared into the forest.

Walking back to the wigwam she shared with an Indian family on the edge of the village, Esther found herself deep in thought: Sabbatis, an Indian known for his cunning and savagery, was good to her; Didias had been unfailingly kind; the other children in camp, though strange in many ways, were still eager to have her join their games. I do not always understand them, Esther thought, crossing the compound, but maybe I seem as strange to them as they do to me. I guess it is just understanding one another that shows us how much alike we really are — all God's children.

On a summer day in 1706 Father Bigot (*bē-gō'*), a Jesuit missionary, was making his rounds of the missions in the Norwidgewock area. The French Jesuits had converted many of the Abenakis to Christianity. As Father Bigot approached the village of Chief Sabbatis, he came upon a young girl gathering cress beside a brook in the depths of the forest. A huge mastiff wandered about nearby, stopping its thorough investigation of the underbrush now and then to drink deeply from the brook.

Suddenly, it lifted its head, water dripping from its jowls; the dog's hackles rose and it growled. The priest stopped before the girl discovered him, and what he saw astonished him. At first he had thought she was an Indian girl, barefooted, her scant dress, a ragged elkskin shift much too short, obviously worn for several years, her hair dark and weighted with grease. Then he looked again more closely, noted the blue eyes, the slender nose, the delicately arched brows. This was no Indian.

He stepped into the trail and smilingly approached her. "Good morning, my child. Where do you live? Where are your people?" He spoke Abenaki.

Startled, Esther dropped her bunch of cress and put her hand on Major's head (she had definitely named her new friend Major). "Good morning," she answered. "I live . . ." confused, she pointed vaguely behind her — "in the camp. I am English."

Father Bigot's eyes brightened. Ah, an English girl, a captive no doubt, poor child. He crossed the brook on stepping-stones to her side. Frightened to find herself standing beside a white man, Esther turned to run, but he put his hand on her arm.

"Do not run away, daughter," he said. "I am your friend. What is your name?"

She looked at his kind face under a thatch of white hair. Surely this man meant no harm. Scarcely above a whisper, though a little relaxed now and interested, she answered, "I am Esther Wheelwright." Often at night she found herself starting up, saying in the darkness, "I am Esther Wheelwright." It was something she must never forget. She repeated it now, in English.

Father Bigot caught his breath. Esther Wheelwright! He knew the search for John Wheelwright's captive daughter had gone on for three years now. It was thought that Esther either had been killed by her captors or had died during the first winter of her captivity when smallpox had ravaged the tribes all along the eastern seaboard. Now here she was, lithe and healthy and straight as smoke rising on a windless day; comely, too, beneath her disguise.

Father Bigot could scarcely believe what he saw and heard. She was a prisoner of war so as a Frenchman he had no right to attempt to return her to the English. But another plan began shaping in his mind.

Together they walked to the camp, the dog still rumbling suspiciously, but here Esther's shyness overcame her again. She ran to her wigwam and for the next few days seldom left it.

Father Bigot was teaching the catechism to the children and some grownups in the crude little chapel of the camp.

During her three years with the Indians Esther had attended some of the chapel services held by the Abenakis who had been converted to Christianity. She was fascinated by the chanting and the sweet scent of the juniper and tallow candles. What were they saying? They were talking to God, she felt sure of that, but what were the words? As her knowledge of the Abenaki language grew, she understood more.

"I like my happy song better," she told Major. "I guess because I've known it such a long, long time." But she did listen and she did try to understand and gradually meanings became clearer. Now spirited, independent little Esther, her first shyness slowly vanishing, stood outside the chapel where she could listen to Father Bigot without being seen herself.

Chief Sabbatis laughed good-naturedly. "She will come in one day," he promised. "She is timid as a fawn but with courage above most Indian girls. She will come, Father, you will see. She is a good child; she knows the Abenaki laws of obedience and does not treat them lightly. Of all the maidens in this camp Esther is a gift from the Great Spirit. Even our harshest old women speak well of her. The big dog you saw with her the day you came sends all the other children screaming to their wigwams at the sight of him. With Esther he is harmless as a baby bird. I think the Great Spirit walks beside her."

3

HOWEVER, if Chief Sabbatis had thought Esther would be prompt to come to catechism classes he was mistaken. More than nine years old now, and with a mind of her own, she weighed and sifted everything she heard Father Bigot say. One day shortly before he was to leave, she went to his wigwam.

The priest was bending over a small pile of books on the ground before him, squinting a little in the dim light as he read. When Esther darkened the doorway, he looked up and a smile of pleased surprise brightened his thin face.

"Esther, my child, how nice! Come in, come in. I was just working on a plan I have for you. Sit down." He moved the books and Esther sat cross-legged on the ground beside them.

Within the last few weeks she had begun to think again of life outside the Indian village. Watching Father Bigot one day as he talked to the children, she noticed how clean his hands were, and looked down at her own small grubby paws clasped in her lap. And once he used the word "French."

What is French, she wondered. There seemed so much to know. The Gospel stories were wonderful, but she wanted to learn more about them. Hungry for knowledge, discontent now replaced the placid submission of the last three years. She must ask questions of someone and Father Bigot obviously was that someone. So, curbing her shyness, she went to his wigwam. In another week it would be too late, for he would be gone. The thought of the camp without him filled her with dismay.

Now, rocking slowly back and forth, hands clasped around her feet, she tried to find words. Finally, she spoke:

"Father, I want to learn — learn *everything*, not just the catechism." Her voice was steady, her blue eyes unwavering.

"Ah? Everything? That is a big order, child. What in particular do you want to learn?" (I am right, Father Bigot thought. This young girl has an unusual mind. She must be educated and taken from here. She could become a brilliant woman.) Aloud he repeated, "What in particular?"

Esther studied the toe of her moccasin. This was not so easy to explain. Then, "Father, tell me where are the people?"

"People? What people, Esther?"

"The other people in the world. We are not all there are, I know. And Our Lord went about the cities. You read us that from the Gospels. Where are the cities? And I know that not everybody everywhere speaks Abenaki, because I can speak English — a little. And are there other ways to speak? And what does the word 'French' mean?"

The effort had been great and Esther's heart was pounding when she finished. Father Bigot ran his fingers through his hair.

40

"I believe God must have sent you here this morning, child," he said after a pause. "Just before you came I had been going over some things I want you to study. French is a beautiful language. Abenaki is not enough. I shall be here another week and you must now start to learn to read French. And we will go over the Creed and the catechism questions, too. When I return I hope all these things will be clear to you and then you can be baptized. I'll bring more books and they will help you learn about people and cities. Will that —— ?" He stopped, for Esther had buried her face in her hands. This was all so much more than she had hoped for.

"Here is a French primer," the priest continued. "Every day until I leave we will go over the lessons. Then when you know the words in the primer, you can begin to read the catechism. The other books can follow."

A week is a short time, but during it Esther concentrated on French. "*Je suis — tu es — il est. Nous sommes — vous êtes — ils sont*," she chanted. "*Où est le chat?*" she demanded of Major who banged his tail and pranced a little, wishing perhaps that he knew where "*le chat*" was. Then Father Bigot was gone, swallowed up in the forest, and Esther was alone with the new joy of learning. His parting promise to her had been that he would bring her a rhyming arithmetic with the other books.

And Sabbatis watched her. Conversion — or the outward signs of it — was all very well for it was rewarded with help from the French; even the conversion of captives had its secondary value. However, there was a quality in Esther's new-found joy in learning that disturbed him. Now her greatest happiness was walking the trails deep into the forest, studying her primer and her catechism. The compulsion to learn filled her days.

Sabbatis thought this was good as far as it went, but was she forgetting the Indian ways that made her so valuable in camp? He remembered that when one of the women had killed and skinned and butchered a camp dog for the common pot during one season of hunger, Esther had screamed and gone limp. Later, though, she too had learned the duties of an Indian woman and performed them well. Now she seemed to have withdrawn into a realm apart from the camp. This was not good, since the Chief had plans for her within the tribe. To sell her to Canada was one thing; she would bring a good price. On the other hand, such a young girl as part of the tribe, married in a few years to a warrior, was worth more than a purchaser would give for her. Sabbatis, though a convert himself, took Christianity lightly and Esther's earnest absorption in its teachings bothered him. If it were not for little Lappawinze, he would have been deeply worried that Esther was forgetting the Indian way and returning to the ways of the white people.

Lappawinze, his three-year-old nephew, the motherless son of his younger brother, adored Esther. Often as she sat in her wigwam sewing moccasins, the boy would search her out.

Chin quivering, little moon face streaked with tears, he would push her work aside, climb into her lap and demand shakily:

"Sing to me, Esther. The big boys are mean and won't let me play with them."

He would bury his face in her neck, dripping tears, and Esther would hold the shaking little brave close. Closing her eyes, she would think of kind Didias and begin singing softly "*He'-hai-gwa'-ni-ho'-yu-wa-ni'*" until the sobs abated and the sturdy little body slumped against her in sleep.

Now this, this was as it should be, Sabbatis told himself whenever he came upon the scene. This was a perfect picture of what he dreamed the future should hold for Esther — a wife and mother in the tribe, beloved by every member.

Only Major did not approve. Whenever he came into the wigwam and found Lappawinze asleep there, he would grumble softly and back out. This was an Indian child and he was suspicious of all Indians no matter what their age.

One day Sabbatis saw Major growl at the little boy as he played with Esther. The Chief was furious. Something must be done. Esther might weep but she would recover. After all, a dog was only a dog. Times were hard, yet the great beast was growing sleek (thanks to the food Esther shared with him) and now he dared resent Lappawinze in Esther's wigwam.

When the first autumn storms came Esther began to suspect that her beloved Major had made dangerous enemies.

43

She had heard some of the men grumbling as they looked from the well-fed dog to the thin stew simmering in the pots.

"They wouldn't dare!" she whispered desperately, her arms around Major's neck, her cheek against his silky ear. But in her heart she knew they would, and with her knowledge a slow burning resentment grew and a dawning determination to live again among her own kind.

Indian summer came with a week of balmy warmth after days of wet snow; the forest was gray now and denuded. Here and there a single crimson leaf swung bravely from the tip of a branch, defying the season and the wind.

One golden morning, Esther, with Major loping about in search of rabbits to chase and Lappawinze happily scuffing leaves beside her, went into the forest looking for late sweet onions and bitter oregano for stew. The waterfall into which the brook emptied roared as it tumbled on the rocks below; here and there a crow cawed high in the dead branches overhead. Esther thought about Father Bigot. When would he come? Would he *ever* come? "I will come back, my child," he had said as he gave her his parting blessing. "Have faith — never lose it — and only good will follow."

Esther shifted the basket she was carrying. Suppose he should never come back? It was a thought that had tormented her for weeks. Who will help me then? I am not even sure I've translated the Creed correctly. And where is "the world?" Only Father can explain it, Father and the books he is bringing me *if* he returns. But that is not having faith. He will come back. "Have faith and only good will follow," he said. He is bound to come. He . . .

Deep in thought, she had not realized that Lappawinze had disappeared. Now she heard a child's voice calling. In a panic she answered.

"Lappawinze, where are you? Answer me!" (Oh, if only I'd made him stay in the camp!) "Lappawinze! Lappawinze!"

She was running now and instinctively she made for the waterfall, shouting, "Major! Major, come quickly! Come, boy!" And through the dead underbrush she heard him crashing toward her as she ran.

At the brook she stopped for a moment, then began following it downstream. But now Major outstripped her, his huge, smoke-colored body blending so perfectly with the dead growth all about that he might have been a ghost. He tore past her and she heard the child's voice again. Heartsick at her carelessness in having let the baby stray away, frantic to reach him, Esther ran after Major. At the head of the water-fall he had stopped, legs braced, and bobbing in the white spray she saw Lappawinze's round little black head.

For just a second Major hesitated then like a gray shadow he vaulted out over the water. "Oh, God, please let Major reach him!" Esther prayed as she watched. "Please, please!"

Major landed with a splash and for a moment Esther could make out nothing but churning water. Then she saw the big dog heading downstream, his head high as he held Lappa-winze by the collar. Then he was scrambling up the embankment and she rushed to the side of the little boy. He was screaming lustily as water poured from his mouth and nose and cascaded from his hair.

"There, there, little warrior," Esther crooned. "Don't cry. We'll go get a dry blanket, then Esther'll sing. Wasn't Major a good dog to help you? Good Major, good dog!" She patted

Major who shook himself until he all but threw himself to the ground, sending a shower in all directions and looking with frank disgust at the little boy who had been the cause of all his discomfort.

Lappawinze's father and another brave, returning from a morning's hunting, heard Esther's cry and came plunging into the clearing just as Major with his dripping burden crawled up the embankment. What happened? they wanted to know, and Esther explained.

"Lappawinze fell into the waterfall. I thought he was just beside me, but he was playing in the leaves and he ran off before I knew what had happened. Then I heard him cry and Major jumped in for him. I'll take him to my wigwam and put a dry blanket around him and I know he'll be all right. He must get dry, though, or he will take cold."

The boy's father, a stocky, rather stolid-looking man, reached for Lappawinze. "Come, my son, we will go to see Sabbatis and tell him what a stupid English girl Esther is."

They set out with Lappawinze, still sobbing, in his father's arms and presently they stood before Sabbatis. The story was quickly told and for the first time Esther saw anger in the Chief's eyes when he turned to her.

"Is this true, Esther? The boy could have drowned. You did not take care. What do you say?"

Esther felt tears welling in her eyes and brushed her sleeve across them. "I am sorry, O Chief," she answered. "I did not mean to be careless. I love Lappawinze. If Major had not been there I don't know what I would have done. Let me get dry clothes for the body and — —"

"No! Lappawinze goes to his father's wigwam. And Major stays here. Go to your wigwam!"

Outraged, Esther turned to go but Lappawinze, who had grown quiet, began to scream again and kick. "I want to go with Esther," he shouted, his feet beating a business-like tattoo against his father's buckskin. "I want to stay with Esther. She can sing."

A look passed between the brothers and a ghost of a smile hovered about Sabbatis's lips. He looked from Esther to the weeping little boy, to the great dog still shaking itself in an afterglow of comfort, and then out of a real sense of justice he spoke.

"Esther, you have forgotten that you are now an Indian maiden and are acting like a silly English girl always with your head in books. You give no thought to the camp and wigwam. As a result the child is nearly drowned. So now you will give up your books until Father Bigot comes again and speaks wisdom to you. You may keep the dog because otherwise he would run away and he has value. Now go to your wigwam and take the child with you. He, too, should be ashamed for he cries like a woman. An Abenaki brave never cries. Go now."

He waved her off and Esther, choking with anger yet admitting unwillingly the justice of Chief Sabbatis's punishment, stumbled across the compound, little Lappawinze clinging to her hand. Ten minutes later the soft music of "*He'-hai-gwa'-ni-ho'-yu-wa-ni'*" floated from her wigwam and Lappawinze, a cocoon, wrapped in a red blanket, lay asleep on the floor.

Once again there was enough corn meal, maize, dried berries, fish and game, and Major was safe — for the time being, at least. Without her books Esther tried to curb her sense of bitter frustration by saying over and over the French sentences she had learned. Thrusting her bone awl into the hide she was using for making moccasins, pulling through the bone needle and dried sinew thread, she prayed for patience: "Dear God, please let Father Bigot come soon. I'm afraid I'll forget."

Just before Christmas when the snow lay deep over the forest he came. His travels had taken him far among the sick and impoverished camps and he looked haggard, his venerable figure painfully thin in its sleazy cassock. There was great rejoicing in camp and drums beat and rattles chattered far into the night. The greatly beloved father had returned.

The following morning there was early Mass, and as Father Bigot caught a glimpse of Esther far at the back of the chapel, he was shocked at the change in her appearance. The lovely dreaming blue eyes had lost much of their life and her face was drawn. After the service he caught up with her as she plodded through the snow to her wigwam. She was overjoyed to see him, yet she dreaded the confession of serious carelessness that she knew she must now make.

49

"Esther, my good child," he greeted her, "I am so glad to see you again, and I've kept my promise. I have brought you more books."

He waited, expecting her usual enthusiastic outburst. Instead she put her hands over her face. "What is it, child? What is wrong?" He tried to take her hands but she only shook her head and kept her face covered.

Finally, while the snow drifted around them and the wind snatched away many of her words, she told her story. "It was my fault, Father," she said, "all my fault. But I do need my books if I am to learn." She hesitated. "I do not want to stay here any more. I do not want to be an Indian. I want to know about people and the world they live in and all the beautiful things in it. Now I want . . . to get away and be what I am supposed to be. Am I wicked, Father?"

He noticed that her hands, though chapped and blue with cold, were clean and that she had washed some of the grease from her face so that a strange-looking English girl peered out from what was now a poor disguise. No wonder Sabbatis was worried.

"No, Esther, you are not wicked; you are growing up. Believe me, I will do my best to take you from here to Quebec. But we must not hope for too much — just pray. I'll speak to Sabbatis today." The old priest wondered just how he was to do this.

Father Bigot looked at the young figure before him, noted

how dark the blue eyes had become as emotion swept over her, and smiled indulgently.

Esther shook her head. "But you will help me to get away. *Please, please*, Father?"

And Father Bigot promised he would.

4

THERE was feasting in the camp all through the day, for a runner had come with news toward midday that a large group of captives was being brought in, and in the evening they came. Many were half frozen, some dying. As though obeying orders which none but she could hear, Esther took a tiny baby from its unconscious mother and fed it warm gruel made of the pounded kernels of walnuts and fine Italian meal boiled together to form a rich, creamlike substance. She poured broth for the aged, made frightened little children laugh and gave comfort and encouragement to their mothers. A wonderful new peace enveloped her; she knew Father Bigot would not fail her; she knew she was at last on a path from which there would be no turning back. And Sabbatis, not knowing the reason for her calm vigilance and activity, gave his approval.

The weather moderated and snow mixed with rain lashed at the wigwam where Sabbatis and Father Bigot sat talking the next day, and as always when serious conversation was in order, they first smoked a pipe together. The unseasonable December rain set the fire sputtering and the tobacco smoke whirling in stifling clouds. Both men were profoundly serious.

"If your Esther could go to Quebec it would be even greater glory for you, O noble Chief Sabbatis, than if you sold her, a prisoner of war, into Canadian service. To be a servant is a poor thing and brings credit to no one, but to be a great lady and to say, 'Chief Sabbatis spoke the words that made this possible' — this would bring honor to you and to all Abenakis." The priest spoke slowly.

"Also, there would be gifts to your people," he continued. "Think well, my brother, she would not be returning to the English but she would be with our good friends in Quebec. She would bring praise to all Abenakis for she is in truth a maiden of the tribe."

He paused, wondering if his last sentence had been wise, and handed the pipe to his host. Cross-legged on the other side of the fire, Sabbatis studied the priest in unblinking concentration. The pulse in his throat beneath a necklace of shells beat strongly, his eyes never for an instant wavered in their focus on the man opposite him. Finally he spoke.

"You have spoken wisely, O Father. The maiden Esther is of all Abenaki maidens the fairest, the purest. Her tongue speaks no evil; her hands are the willing servants of her gentle heart. She is a rare blossom sprung from a poisonous weed. Now she is ours. No, Father, we who have nourished her through the years will keep her." There was stubborn finality in his tone.

"But perhaps Sabbatis does not quite understand my words." Father Bigot's heart sank at the Indian's steely determination. "Esther would come to visit her Abenaki friends often. She would not leave you; she would bring much joy to you through the gifts the Governor will give you. And to our friends in Quebec she will tell of the kindness and wisdom of the Abenakis. Truly, she will do your tribe proud."

Sabbatis held up his hand. "I have spoken," he said. "The maiden Esther stays with my people. She is promised to one of our bravest warriors when she reaches woman's estate. Her days will be spent with the Abenakis. It has been so spoken in our councils. There can be no change."

So Father Bigot was forced to admit that for the present at least he had failed. "But do not despair, my daughter," he encouraged. "We shall pray. There is yet time. After all, you are not quite twelve years old. Have patience — have faith. All things can be won through faith if it be strong enough."

To Esther the disappointment was shattering. Her hopes had been so high when Father Bigot had returned. Now he was leaving again and she might not see him for many months. Her books had been returned to her by Sabbatis. And Father Bigot had added a copybook for doing sums, a simple history of France and a child's geography. She handled them almost reverently. "I'll learn from you," she whispered, smoothing the cover of a copybook.

She continued to do her share of the work in the camp. She carried the heavy pails of water from the brook for cooking; with the younger women she pounded and kneaded and chewed the pelts of deer and moose to make into clothing; she sewed moccasins and jackets, and taught the younger children to sew. And often, with Lappawinze trotting beside her, she went to the chapel to dust and arrange the flowers on the altar, humming softly to herself as she did. When the earliest spring flowers bloomed — the violets and the wild plum — she put them in large shells and clay pots and placed them near the crucifix.

Her naturally optimistic, merry nature forbade her to sulk, though often when alone in the woods with only Major to hear, she did give vent to her feelings. "I hate this place! We must not stay here!" she confided. "Someday we'll go away, Major, and Sabbatis will never find us. He's kind but we must not stay here always. We are not Indians. Do you understand?" Perhaps Major did, for he whined and dashed off in what looked like an upsurge of great glee. Easter came and Esther taught the children to sing the beautiful *O Salutaris Hostia*. Father Bigot had given her the Abenaki words and on Easter morning when the sweet young voices rose in the anthem, with Esther's clear soprano leading them, several grown-up voices shouted, "Sing it again," and all joined in the singing when once more it began. The Abenaki translation of the verse was:

Kighist wi-nuanurwinns
Spem kik papli go ii domek
Nemiani wi kwidan ghabeuk
Taha saii grihine.

Esther felt as she watched the faces around her that the hymn had meant more to the camp than many sermons. That Easter morning she prayed, "God, my Father, take me from this place. Help me to serve Thee in better ways."

So a year passed and part of another.

During all this time other efforts seem to have been made for the rescue of Esther but nothing came of them. A Lieutenant Josiah Littlefield of Wells, who must have known the Wheelwrights, was captured by Indians in 1708. He may have been one of the captives brought from time to time to Chief Sabbatis's camp, for he wrote from Montreal asking that two Indian captives be sent in exchange for himself and "the Whilerite child." The lieutenant was released only to be killed two years later. But nothing was ever heard of an exchange of prisoners, though John Wheelwright did send an Indian boy north to be exchanged for Esther.

The Marquis de Vaudreuil, the French Governor of Canada, was a man of keen sensibilities and interest in his fellow men. The war between France and England for possession of North American territory and the part in it played by the Indians were matters of the greatest concern to him. Whenever he was able, without jeopardizing the cause of France, he interceded for prisoners.

His wife, the beautiful Marquise, had been summoned to Paris to tutor the royal children. Her boxes were already piled in the corridor of the château and it remained only to decide upon a safe and reliable ship for her to be on her way. Considering that she was the mother of twelve girls and boys ranging in age from a two-year-old toddler to three young men sons, her beauty and youthful gaiety were all the more remarkable. Not only was she beautiful and gay but her wisdom and tact in sharing her husband's good works made her a beloved woman throughout the country. Both she and the Marquis had known Father Bigot for years. And now he needed their help.

He was determined that Esther should be freed, yet there seemed no way of moving Sabbatis from his intention to keep her. She was twelve now, and fearing that the Chief might suddenly force her to marry, the priest took his problem to Governor de Vaudreuil. He had only his faith to sustain him, for this was a matter calling for the most skillful bargaining and the Governor, not wishing to rouse the enmity of the great Chief, must act slowly, carefully.

When consulted the Marquise looked skeptical. "Is the child comely? And how about her manners?"

The Marquis shrugged. "According to Father Bigot her manners are perfect. Of course, I haven't seen the child but I like what I've heard."

"Well then, by all means let us see that she is brought to Quebec." His wife was smiling happily as she always did when she was pleased with a plan. "John Wheelwright, her father, is apparently a man of substance and if Esther is at all obedient we should do what we can for her. After all, this war will not go on forever — she will not always be a prisoner of war. Yes, Esther should be brought to Quebec. She can attend the convent school with our Louise and meanwhile look upon this as her home. It would give her the background she needs after her years with the Indians. School girls can be critical and cruel with other girls whom they consider to be outside their own *milieu*."

Her husband, fingering his snuffbox, looked uncertain. "Sabbatis is a powerful man and at the moment I dare not antagonize him. In this wretched war we owe the Indians so much. They have been wonderful allies."

"But if you make it worth Sabbatis's trouble to release Esther — pay him well — after all, you've done it before. I think it is important to get this child from the Indians before she is older and less able to change her ways if they need changing. Of course, if she has become an unmanageable savage, naturally we cannot impose her upon the Sisters, but from what you tell me, Father Bigot says she cannot be too bad. Act promptly, my dear. That is my advice." The Marquise patted her husband's shoulder encouragingly and he lifted her fingers to his lips.

Winter had come again and the Abenakis had broken camp and moved farther west and north to the shore of what is now Wyman Lake where hunting was good and the hills formed protection against blizzards. The winter, however, was mild and wet and many of the Indians suffered from influenza, Esther among them. She had tried with all her might not to become discouraged, but as the months and then a year passed she began to wonder if Father Bigot had died. Once a young priest had come to the mission to say Mass and preach and from him she learned that her beloved friend had been ill some months earlier. Beyond that she knew nothing. But he was an old man and his work both tiring and dangerous, and fear like a thorn hidden in her clothing began to torment Esther.

"All things can be won through faith," Father Bigot had promised, and she never had let her faith grow dim. But now, sick and miserable, she found it hard to be optimistic.

Shivering feverishly she huddled in her blankets, trying to sew, yet her fingers seemed to have lost their knack of twisting the awl. Her head throbbed and dreams like wisps of smoke drifted through her consciousness. In them she glimpsed the flicker of candles, heard their soft whisper, and from far off a familiar chanting. Would Father Bigot ever come? Where was he? Would she ever be free? She laid aside her sewing and picked up her French grammar and tried to read. But the lines blurred, and heartsick, she laid it down while the slow tears dropped on her deerskin shirt.

Suddenly — what was that? She must be very sick for she had heard a voice she knew could not be there — Father Bigot's! She scrambled to her feet, her fever-flushed face aglow. "Father! Father, I'm here!" He had come. This was no dream. It was his voice she heard. And even while she struggled toward the entrance of the wigwam, the door flap lifted and he stood before her, more fragile and gaunt-looking than when she had last seen him, but smiling in deep content.

He held out both hands and, tripping over the impeding blanket, she caught them in hers and fell weeping on her knees before him. He raised her gently to her feet. "Esther, Esther, my dear child, how you have grown — as the larkspur shoots up almost overnight from a small green promise. But, come, you are ill and it is cold — I see your fire is out. Sabbatis tells me more than half the camp is down with this wretched influenza. However, God is good. Your wait is over. You have had faith? I think you must have had."

Esther scarcely dared breathe as hope and dread of new disappointment struggled for first place in her mind. Her head throbbing with fever, her body trembling with weakness, she made her eyes meet his. "Father, then you mean . . .?"

"Yes, I've come to take you to Quebec."

"But Sabbatis? The women have been working since the moon of the ripening corn on my bridal dress of white elkskin and we have danced the dance of betrothal — the whole camp — and — —"

"Never mind that. Some other maiden can wear the gown,

and there can be another dance one day. Our Governor, the Marquis de Vaudreuil, has sent a fortune to Sabbatis: knives, guns, rum, sugar, cloth, slaughtered swine and sheep and bags of silver. He is now a very rich man and because he is also a man of honor you are released. As soon as you can travel we will start on our journey."

For a full minute Esther could only stare at him in unbelief. The wonder of it was almost too much for the sick girl. She could only bury her face in her hands, whispering, "Thank God! Oh, thank God!" For this she had faithfully studied the books Father Bigot had left her; for this she had learned to speak a halting French.

She was close to hysteria and the gentle priest put his arm about her shoulder to steady her. "You must rest, Esther, and keep warm. The skies seem to be clearing and within a week the weather should be good for traveling. Sabbatis will send a woman with you to carry your bundle. The de Vaudreuils, the Marquise, Louise de Vaudreuil who is your age, all are waiting to welcome you among them. But now, come, lie down, put the sewing away and sleep. You must build up your strength. I shall be with Sabbatis if you need me." Gently he lowered her to her bed, tucked the bearskin about her and left her. Esther found she could not sleep. Every heartbeat seemed to shout, "Thank God! Thank God! Thank God!" Finally she took up her sewing again and far into the night by the light of the fire she continued to work. Faith had given its answer.

In his wigwam with two of his braves, Sabbatis went over and over his treasure, scarcely able to believe his good fortune, though naggingly aware of the sacrifice it had cost him in the loss of Esther. Would there ever again be such a maiden? He doubted it — and yet, he looked at the ransom. He ran his finger along the polished blade of a knife and smiled. There would be other maidens; the young warrior who would have had Esther must wait.

5

PARTINGS and farewells, no matter how eagerly they may be awaited, still usually bring some heartache. So it was with Esther. Two weeks later, wrapped in one of her favorite blankets, she stood beside Father Bigot in the pale light of dawn to say farewell to the Abenaki camp. Lappawinze clung to her hand and was trying desperately to keep his promise not to cry. Once he looked up at her, his chin quivering. "Esther, come back. When I am a big warrior I will *bring* Esther back." And Esther assured him that was quite right.

But another problem was not so easily solved. At the other end of the compound, tied in Sabbatis's wigwam, Major barked his dismay at being left behind.

"It cannot be helped, my daughter," Father Bigot reasoned with Esther, watching her as she forced back tears. "We cannot possibly take Major. We are carrying just enough food to see us through if we are successful with our fishing and trapping on the way. We could not possibly feed a big dog, too.

64

Besides, we shall be passing through dangerous country and Major's barking at the wrong time might well cost us our lives."

"But will he be well cared for here? You remember how thin he was when he first came to me?" Esther tried not to hear the frantic barking.

"Yes, I am sure he will be. Remember, he saved the boy's life and Sabbatis will not forget."

With this Esther had to be satisfied. She said her final good-bys, and then, after Father Bigot had given the camp his blessing, she and Arosen, the woman who was to go with them, picked up their bundles and followed him up the trail and into the forest. Two Indians paddled them across the lake which fortunately was not frozen, the early spring rains having washed the woods and waterways almost clear of snow and ice. Then the travelers bade their guides good-by and struck out for themselves. To Father Bigot every mile of the way was familiar.

At the end of two hours Esther admitted ruefully that she could go no farther, so they rested, pushed on, and rested again, and by nightfall had covered a fair distance. The days and nights followed one another in unchanging order: travel, rest, travel, rest and eat, travel to nightfall and sleep. Once Father Bigot, in the lead, stopped suddenly and held up his hand. They had come close to stumbling into the camp of the warring Hurons. By back-tracking and making a wide circle they were able to go on and Esther laughingly declared, "Per-

haps I ought to give thanks by singing my 'happy song'!"
Father Bigot knew she was enjoying her little joke, but not
Arosen. "If you sing the Hurons will hear and kill us all.
You are a foolish girl!"

As her strength returned Esther was able to travel faster
and more easily. In late March, bewildered by the sights and
sounds of a city around her, she stood before the great door
of the Governor's house in Quebec.

Ushered into the rotunda with its sparkling chandelier, many mirrors and soft carpets, Esther caught her breath in combined wonder and nervousness. Putting down her bundle, she pressed her fingertips for a second into the beautiful carpet to make sure it was as soft as it felt to her moccasined feet. It was. Arosen followed suit and, encouraged, sat down cross-legged beside her bundle. Father Bigot ordered her to her feet and she had just obeyed grumbling, when a door opened and the most beautiful being Esther ever had seen came floating toward them, smiling.

Esther had rehearsed the introduction with Father Bigot many times but even so, her voice shook and Abenaki words somehow entangled themselves with the carefully memorized French. This lovely lady was the Marquise de Vaudreuil, so beautiful, so kind, and this palace-like dwelling was her home. Esther listened while the Marquise and Father Bigot talked but the words came with such lightning speed that she could not follow and in another moment he had given her his blessing and was gone, taking Arosen with him.

The Marquise touched a bell and two women entered whom she addressed as Paulette and Genevieve. Then the Marquise too, patted Esther's shoulder and left. Paulette was young and plump and rosy-cheeked and her smile was merry as she approached Esther.

"You must be weary, child," she said, picking up the bundles. "You have had a long, hard journey, but some warm food and a good bath will refresh you. I'll be back directly.

Meanwhile I will prepare the small chamber and the bath as well."

When she had gone, Genevieve gently, tactfully tried to put Esther at ease, asking about her journey and the camp, but Esther's mind was in too great turmoil to permit her to make sensible answers and she answered in monosyllables lest she burst into tears from sheer panic.

The odor of rancid bear grease poured from the frightened girl like the stench from a wild animal long dead, and vermin were apparent in the grease-darkened hair. Yet Esther, used to the Indian way of life, believed a reasonably clean face and hands represented real cleanliness. The little girl in starched pinafore and snug linsey-woolsey had disappeared, lost in almost six years of savage existence. Now what, she wondered, was meant by "the small chamber" and "the bath as well"? What were they going to do to her?

Obediently she drank the broth which Genevieve gave her, and as she savored its spicy goodness she looked about the classically beautiful room. No, no, she told herself with what assurance she could muster, people who lived in such places — such gentle, smiling people — did not torture one like the Hurons. Or did they? Father Bigot had not thought so or he would not have brought her here in the first place.

Paulette returned now. Hand outstretched almost as one would to a shy kitten, she said, "Come now, a hot bath is ready. Then you must go to bed and rest."

She spoke French and only two words stood out clearly to

Esther. Sheer terror rooted her feet to the floor. "What is that, please, Madame?" she queried. "A bath is hot water, is it not? You would kill me perhaps?"

The young woman smiled broadly and took her hand. "No, no, no, my child," she comforted. "A hot bath is to make you comfortable. And we must rid you of that hair. You will see how much happier you will be. Come, now."

Esther followed Paulette into a small room which seemed to be directly off the kitchen and scullery. It was very warm and in the middle of the floor stood an enormous wooden tub filled with steaming water. Beside it, looking rather like a jolly executioner in her big white apron, stood another maid merrily brandishing a pair of scissors.

Only the stoicism born of life in the wilderness kept Esther from screaming as she felt the scissors and then a razor on her head; only years of submission induced her to let them help her into the tub and endure Paulette's energetic wielding of a brush and strong soap.

"That feels better, no, *petite*?" Paulette was wrapping her in a huge soft towel. "Now up we go to a bath you will love." While the maid put the little room to rights, Paulette led Esther up a flight of stairs and opened a door into what the dazed girl believed must be an anteroom to heaven itself. Here were white marble, exquisite jars and bottles, soft sponges, scented soaps.

Her skin still burning from Paulette's scrubbing, Esther was delighted to slip into the scented water for a final bath and shampoo, to have soothing oil rubbed on her tingling body and finally to let Paulette slip a snowy white linen shift over her head. She could not remember falling sleep but her awakening in a soft white bed many hours later was in itself, she thought, a foretaste of heaven.

"Hello — I am Louise." The girl standing at the foot of the bed had dark eyes and curly black hair. Her rather large mouth was spread in a wide grin and her warm friendliness was reassuring. "You are going to school with me next week and today we can go to Mass together."

Her diction was beautiful, and perhaps thinking of Esther's slight knowledge of the French language, she thoughtfully spoke very slowly and Esther understood her perfectly. She sat up in bed, marveling at her white hands and the wonderful feeling of cleanliness over her entire body. Then she put her hands to her head and shrank at the touch of her bristly skull.

"Oh, I must look terrible! How can I go to Mass looking so?"

Louise broke into a ripple of laughter and Esther found herself joining her. "No, my friend, you do not look terrible. You look like a handsome boy. So now, you cannot be angry at that?"

"No," Esther found herself saying hesitantly, "why should I be angry? It is all so new to me, but if you will help me I know I can learn even to like my funny head!"

Paulette, entering with her arms full of clothes, stopped on the threshold, beaming. "Ah, you see, you see, we were right:

70

what wonders a hot bath does! Now our little friend is laughing and happy and only yesterday she was so weary she fell asleep before we could get her to bed."

She spread an array of dresses and chemises out on a chair. "These are for you to try on. They are Mademoiselle's but I think they will fit you. Then here" — she tugged at the cover of a box — "is a bonnet which will fit down over your head and not show what we did to you. Come now, it will be time to leave for Mass in just a little while. I will help you with these and then you must have chocolate."

Dressed in becoming clothes, seated beside the Marquise in the Governor's pew, Esther tried to follow the order of the Mass, but she found she could not. Only yesterday she had been a tired, filthy wanderer without even the slightest idea of what wealth and beauty could mean. Today, well fed and clothed, she sat beside Canada's first family listening to the magnificent thunder of the organ and the glorious voices of the choir of men and boys, filling her eyes with the beauty of the altar with its countless lights, its gold and silver vessels and the rich vestments of the celebrant. The change had been too great and it had all come too suddenly. She could only kneel in stunned wonder. And when at Benediction after Mass, the congregation and the choir sang *O Salutaris Hostia* she found herself singing the Abenaki words, tears sliding unheeded down her cheeks.

Meanwhile matters at the château were moving with orderly speed. The Marquise's ship had been decided upon and she would sail within a few days. Of her twelve children the younger girls and boys would be left in the care of their governess under their father's supervision; two of the older boys were studying at the University of Paris, the Sorbonne; and Philippe, the oldest son, was in the army.

After giving the matter careful thought the Marquise felt it wisest to have Louise and Esther live at the convent, returning to the château on state occasions or feast days. For the Marquis — gentle, kindly soul that he was — to have two active girls constantly under foot and to be responsible for them would have been wearing, so the Marquise made her decision.

"Remember," she said the evening before she embarked, "I shall not be away forever. While I am gone, Louise, I want you to take Esther under your wing and see that she is not only happy here in Quebec but that she improves herself in every possible way. When she returns to her parents, as she will after the war, she must be a credit to our care."

Louise slipped her arm through Esther's. "Never you mind, Mother," she laughed, "our Esther is very dear to me and though I shall not be too strict with her I shall not spoil her either, eh, Esther? I shall teach you to speak French and I shall not let you blow in your soup. When Mother comes back she will not know you."

"I shall try very hard, Madame," Esther promised. "So much that is wonderful has happened to me because of your kindness, yours and Monsieur your husband's, that I shall never be able to repay you. Louise loves to tease" — and now she was laughing, too — "but there will be no more blowing of the soup."

So the Marquise de Vaudreuil sailed for France and Esther was entered as a boarding pupil in the Ursuline convent. Louise, though several classes ahead of her, still watched over her like a mother hen. The year was 1709 and Esther had almost reached her thirteenth birthday.

The months moved on. At first adjustment to life at the convent was not easy to the girl who knew nothing of civilization, but her short time with the de Vaudreuils had given her a smattering of poise and Louise's constant friendship did help. Nevertheless she was painfully shy before the other girls, conscious of her awkwardness, her lack of knowledge. For many weeks knives and forks remained a puzzle, slipping from her fingers to clatter to the floor while other girls at the table giggled. After a time the private lessons she had in table manners began to show results, but meanwhile each meal was an ordeal.

Her strange appearance with her sheared head and Louise's borrowed clothes which lacked something in fit did not bother Esther. She was unaware of it. She tried to make friends with the few Indian girls who were pupils in the convent, but made little headway as they refused to be drawn out.

But she was learning how very important education was, so she curbed her impatience and disappointment and applied

73

herself to her studies and presently was leading her class.

Soon Esther was fourteen, a singularly lovely-looking girl with a head of short golden curls and the serene expression of an angel in a painting by Veronese. As time passed and she became surer of herself she developed a delightful sense of humor that kept the girls in gales of laughter and brought smiles to the faces of even the sternest nuns. But in spite of her bubbling humor, Esther now began to dream of the day when she would be wearing the habit of an Ursuline nun. She gave every waking moment to her studies, perfecting her penmanship, reading and learning to appreciate the classics. She was completely happy with her books. Her French diction never quite lost a slight guttural slur and in moments of agitation or embarrassment she was apt to revert to the Indian abruptness of speech so inconsistent with her delicate beauty and gentleness.

It was not strange that she should have become a favorite with the nuns. Her humility, her indifference to the ridicule she suffered during her first weeks at the convent, and her complete unconsciousness of her budding beauty and her outstanding scholarship all earned her a high place in their affection. And in one girl at least it roused a bitter jealousy.

Veronique La Tour was a handsome girl whose father, a general in the army, was also a man of great wealth whose holdings comprised some of the valuable land in and around the Upper City. Though an indifferent scholar, Veronique by her many gifts to the convent and her many attentions to the nuns, had come to fancy herself a person of importance in the school and resented the presence of anyone who might threaten that position. Then Esther came, Esther with nothing to give but her sincere efforts and devotion and fine scholarship. Veronique's jealous dislike of her was instant and vicious though she took care to hide it. Esther, not realizing that she was only making matters worse, tried to be friendly and went so far as to offer to help Veronique in the subjects that were hard for her, arithmetic among them. With well-concealed contempt Veronique declined the offer.

A test was given in mathematics, not Esther's best subject, and as the Sister in charge was one of the strictest in the convent and the test a hard one, all the girls were very worried. After several hours of concentrated effort Esther looked at her finished sheet of questions and answers and sighed. It did not please her but it was the best she could do. She left it on her desk as they had been instructed to do and went to her room to prepare for the afternoon's test in religion.

Veronique, across the aisle, looked from her own blank sheets to Esther's carefully worked out problems and muttered to herself, "That bold Indian girl has all the answers and I not one!" She sat for a moment, her eyes moving busily from one paper to the other, then, "We'll see!" In her eagerness she almost spoke aloud.

It was simple. She stood up and as she turned she brushed her skirt against Esther's desk, quickly slipping her examination paper into its folds, and went to the recreation room across the hall. Just as she thought, there was no one there. Half an hour later she was back, Esther's paper snugly hidden beneath a book which she carefully put on Esther's desk. Then she crossed the aisle and began leisurely to straighten up her own desk.

The Sister in charge looked up from the work she was correcting.

"But you know, Veronique, that you are not to leave the room during examinations?" She smiled at Veronique.

Veronique smiled back, her voice a little shaky when she answered.

"Yes, Sister, I know. Please forgive me. I thought it did not matter since I have finished my paper and was just gathering material for the examination this afternoon."

"Very well, never mind. Clear your desk; it is growing late." (That is a lovely child, she thought as she settled back to her work.)

Two days later, as was customary, she discussed the results of the test with the class, speaking to each girl in turn.

"And you, Veronique, how did you find the test? Your paper was well filled and I found it very interesting. Did you have any difficulties?"

Veronique looked up, flushed and smiling. "No, Sister" — her voice was not quite steady — "I had no trouble. The test seemed quite simple."

The nun looked at her for a long moment, then passed on to another pupil. Finally she reached Esther.

76

Esther had been dreading the interview, for in spite of her careful work she did not have too much faith in the results, and her blue eyes darkened as they always did when she was nervous. A geometry theorem always puzzled her to begin with, then working her way through the mazes of it was even worse. Now after an examination, which taxed every ounce of concentration she could muster, she dreaded hearing the teacher's comments on her work.

She heard the Sister's voice and there was a stern note in it. Yes, the severity was there and seemed to be meant for her.

"Now, Esther," the nun was saying, "suppose you tell us how you felt about the test. Were there things about it that you did not understand? Are you sure you could do it again if you were asked to?"

Esther's heart was pounding furiously. What had she done? Was her paper so poor that she was going to be asked to do it over? How badly had she failed? But the Sister was speaking again, calmly, slowly, yet with a rising inflection in almost everything she said as though she were asking questions instead of making statements.

"Young ladies," the words came clearly, distinctly, "the test you took the day before yesterday was the most difficult of the year. Some of the problems were not unusually hard, and I may say that most of you answered them correctly. There was one, however, number eight, which I had grave doubts any of you would be able to manage." She turned to Esther again and continued to look at her as she spoke. "Two girls, however, did answer it almost correctly, not only correctly but identically, Esther Wheelwright and Veronique La Tour."

As she looked at the two girls, Esther looked back in frank surprise. Veronique, her face crimson, her lips compressed to hide their quivering, riffled the pages of the book on her desk. "Identically" — what did Sister mean?

"Veronique, suppose you take your paper and explain to the class the one small hidden mistake there is in it. Esther, will you pass out the other papers so the girls may compare their answers? This is a problem from which I think we may all learn much."

Smiling coolly, she handed the sheaf of papers to Esther who began distributing them. Esther was still mystified that she should have given so nearly perfect an answer to wretched "number eight" but even more surprised that Veronique should have done the same thing — and what mistake had they made, what *identical* mistake?

"Veronique?" Sister folded her hands, waiting.

Veronique got to her feet, cleared her throat. "I — I do not see any mistake, Sister," she faltered. "I thought the problem quite clear. Maybe Esther didn't — perhaps she . . ."

"Very well, then, analyze it step by step for us that we may profit by your skill."

There was a long silence. Veronique sat down, wordlessly shaking her head. Her knees failed her.

"Esther, will you analyze the problem and point out the

mistake in your answer? Veronique does not seem to be able to." Faced with an obvious example of dishonesty, the nun was loath to place the blame on either girl, yet for both their sakes she felt the ugly truth must be brought into the open.

Esther ran her eyes down over her work and immediately saw the silly mistake which had prevented her examination from being perfect. Clearly she went over the example and pointed out her error and was still speaking when there was an interruption.

Veronique slid from her seat and ran out of the room. What happened next no one knew. She must have tripped on the top of the polished flight of stairs leading down to the reception floor. There was a muffled scream and the horrified girls heard her fall over and over to the bottom of the flight.

Esther was the first to reach her, and with the sure instinct of the protector which she had shown so often in the Abenaki camp, she bent over her rival, murmuring comfort. Veronique's ankle was broken, and days and nights of pain for the unhappy girl followed. But strangely enough under the circumstances, it was Esther she wanted beside her, Esther alone who could bring comfort. When sleepless nights made the sick girl restless, a soft crooning came from her room and the Abenaki words of little Lappawinze's favorite song: "*He'-hai-gwa'-ni-ho'-yu-wa-ni'.*" The examination papers were never mentioned again.

6

ESTHER bloomed under the peaceful, orderly routine of the convent. By nature a student, she loved her work and made great strides in it. She was giving much thought to her confirmation, too, and when she knelt before the bishop and felt his hands placed in blessing over her head she knew a joy so profound, so intense, that for moments she felt transformed into another world. For her first Communion Louise had given her a beautiful prayer book, dark blue leather with a tiny chased gold cross, an anchor, and a heart on its ribbon markers, and as she followed the prayers of the Mass she knew that someday she would wear the habit of the Ursulines.

But the conscience of the Marquis de Vaudreuil was troubling him. He felt wholly responsible for Esther who now seemed determined to enter the cloister. The Ursuline nuns were his friends and supporters and to offend them was his last thought. On the other hand, Esther had seen little of the social life of Quebec. If eventually she was to be returned to her parents, as he hoped she would be, it could not be as a Roman Catholic nun. At any rate she must see more of the outside world to be absolutely certain she wanted above all things to leave it for the cloister. He finally took himself to the convent for a long talk with the Mother Superior, a woman of great wisdom and common sense.

"Permit me, Mother," he addressed the austere lady looking at him from under her snowy coif, "to take our young friend to the château for a time. There are governesses there to watch over her and at the same time she will be exposed to the ways of the world, to the possibility of making a good marriage. She and Louise can share their amusements as well as their devotions. After, let us say, six months Esther should be much surer of herself than she is now, though she would never admit that. And meanwhile, since the war should soon be over, I really feel I must try to get in touch with Esther's family. Soon she will no longer be a prisoner of war, and her parents must judge for her — not we."

The Reverend Mother nodded gravely. "I do understand perfectly, my lord, though I doubt anything will ever swerve Esther from the course she has set her heart on. I'll speak to her and see that she comes to the château at the end of the week."

"But I am so happy here, Reverend Mother," Esther objected a few hours later when she stood beside the Mother Superior's desk and heard her proposal. "I love Louise, and her father always has treated me as one of the family, but *this*

is my home, not the château. *Must* I go?" Her eyes were dark with pleading.

"Yes, my dear child, I think you must. After all, the Marquis is a very wise man, and what he proposes is only for a few months. He is our Governor and he has been so very generous to the convent and the school and I think he would be gravely hurt if you refused to coöperate with him in his plan."

So the end of the week found Esther tucked into the glittering coach with the de Vaudreuil crest upon its doors, driving with Louise to the château. Her heart was heavy as they rolled away from the convent; it was the place she loved above any other. Yet, she was after all a young girl starved for beauty without knowing it. Her first brief stay with the de Vaudreuils had been so fraught with bewilderment and unease that she had scarcely been aware of her surroundings. But now as she tiptoed around her room breathlessly touching the exquisite scent bottles, the rose satin counterpane on the bed with its lacy canopy, the porcelain potpourri sending forth its spicy scent, she flushed with a new, hitherto-unknown delight.

Now the happy weeks flew. Each morning the two girls were driven to their classes at the convent; each afternoon they returned to the château, chattering, laughing, full of the day's activities. The evenings as a rule were given over to festivities for the young people. Guests from other great houses came to take part in the charades and to dance the popular minuet. And during the final week of Esther's first month at the château an event occurred which opened an entirely new concept of what life outside the convent could mean.

Young Count Philippe de Vaudreuil came home on leave from the army. Louise had written him repeatedly about her little "Indian" friend, Esther, not realizing how often she had all unwittingly stressed the word "Indian." She had given the impression to the brother who read her letters quickly and offhandedly that the girl she mentioned was actually an Abenaki Indian girl.

On the evening of his arrival his father gave a party in his honor, a party which began with dancing at nine and ended with a gala supper long after midnight. Twenty, very handsome in his plum brocade and silver buckles, he had been reconciled to meeting and doing his share toward the entertainment of his young sister's "Indian" friend. It would be a great bore, he admitted, but it would soon be over and he would do his best.

He was standing talking to a fellow officer who had come home with him for a two weeks' visit and was laughingly warning him of the "Indian" *mademoiselle* with whom they were pledged to dance once. Once, he added, would satisfy Louise who seemed to be so very fond of her; after that they had their choice of several dozen lovely belles of the capital. Still laughing, he chanced to look toward the door and caught his breath.

Entering, satin panniers swaying, yellow ringlets bobbing above and around the velvet bandeau holding them, came an exquisite little creature who might have been a Dresden figurine suddenly come to life. Dimples played in her pink cheeks, blue eyes sparkled above the delicate lace fan she held with one hand while the other rested lightly on the Marquis's arm. Was there ever a more alluring little figure? A more provocative smile?

Philippe deserted his friend who trailed after him toward the Marquis, and to their dismay they saw that they were already being crowded out by their appreciative friends. Music for the minuet had just begun and couples were forming in groups around the room.

"Papa — please" — the Count elbowed his way to the front — "please present me."

The Marquis grinned like a schoolboy behind his white moustache and patted Esther's hand. "Mademoiselle Wheelwright, permit me to introduce my son, Philippe, Count de Vaudreuil. I was about to claim this dance myself but perhaps you two would prefer that I waited until later, eh?" He released his little companion and Philippe, bowing low, took her hand.

"That Louise should have warned me!" he managed to say softly as they moved through the stately dance. "May I have the next — and possibly the next?"

She smiled up at him mischievously. "You will not want them, my lord, for Louise's dancing teacher had time to teach

86

me only the minuet. I should slip and fall and disgrace us all if I tried anything else."

"Then all the minuets — please?" He almost missed a step in his eagerness. "Then tomorrow and as long as my leave lasts I'll teach you others — my favorite pavanne and the new allemande. May I?" She nodded, counting carefully.

The Marquis watched approvingly. This fragile little Esther Wheelwright was truly a lovely creature. English she might be, but charming withal and of a good family and a devout Catholic. Her dowry would be considerable, too. Philippe was discerning. Indeed Philippe was more than discerning; he was very much in love.

And Esther? Never had she been so happy. She was enjoying herself with her whole heart. The lively tunes she danced to through the evenings — the dances Philippe taught her; the admiration she saw in the faces of the young gallants who complimented and flattered and begged for a flower from her nosegays; the rich, delicious food that heaped her plate at every meal; the downy, lace-hung bed into which she sank at night, all this made up her life at the château. Her prayers were devout but they were not all-absorbing.

With the memory of her own family so vague, she found it easy to become deeply devoted to the de Vaudreuils, and when the Marquis announced that at last he was making strides in reaching John Wheelwright, she was somewhat uneasy. Both her mother and father had become shadowy figures of the past. Their faces and personalities were lost in the mists of time. Chief Sabbatis was more real.

She felt she was drifting, letting her heart betray her. Philippe sat beside her at church, walked sedately with her and a chaperone along the fortifications, and one day he spoke his love.

Esther was taking a short cut to her room through a narrow passageway leading from the nursery where she and Louise had been having tea with the younger children. As she hurried along the passage, a door halfway down its length opened and Philippe entered. He had been riding, his fair hair blown, gloves and crop still in his hand as he hurried toward her, unseeing, in the semi-darkness. Suddenly they faced each other and suddenly barriers collapsed. Esther was in his arms and he was whispering all the pent-up yearnings of months against her lips. She could only cling to him whispering, "Philippe — Philippe. No. No." Then she tore herself away and ran to her room, heart pounding, cheeks aflame.

What have I done! What sort of weakling am I! The torturing thoughts accused her as she lay on her bed looking into the evening dusk. I must leave here and go back to the convent — this is not my life — not my home. Am I forgetting the very thing I love and want most of life?

However, Philippe would not be put off. Shortly after their encounter in the corridor, Esther found herself alone with him when Louise left them together one morning on the terrace.

"But surely, Esther," he coaxed, "you who have danced so gaily with me, who have been the merriest of us all — ah, my darling, think well before you shut yourself away from life. You were made for beauty and joy — to see and be seen by the great and distinguished in this world. Please, I beg of you, reconsider! Marry me, Esther. I'll take you to France where you will see the glories of Versailles and Fontainebleau, be presented to their Majesties . . ."

She shook her head and put her hand on his arm. "Philippe," she said, "you forget that in the life I shall embrace there will be glories far surpassing those at the Court of France, that my presentation, if I merit it, will be to One far greater than their Majesties. My time of merry-making is over. Believe me, I shall always hold your friendship very dear. You will remember that, Philippe?" Philippe de Vaudreuil would always remember.

Now came a time of confusion, two years of uncertainty and mental anguish for the young girl who wanted to follow the dictates of her vocation. They were years of bitter trial for Esther, and she was shunted from Quebec, to Montreal, to Three Rivers. Sometimes she spent happy weeks with her beloved Ursulines in Quebec. She never lost heart. Somehow, she knew a way would be found to allow her to enter the convent. And at last, on October 2, 1712, her prayers were answered and she returned to the convent to begin her novitiate.

Meanwhile, the Marquis had written to her father, and in

return had received letters expressing his joy and that of his wife at Esther's safety, but quite reasonably they were grieved that she should have been drawn away from her Puritan faith. Their letters were filled with expressions of love and of gratitude for her deliverance from the Indians, but they implored her to reconsider taking the veil.

Then on April 11, 1713, the Treaty of Utrecht was signed ending the war between France and England, and the long task of exchanging prisoners began. The treaty stipulated that any English prisoner who had become a permanent member of the Catholic community in Canada should have full liberty to remain there. This was all very well, but Esther was not yet of age. At the beginning of her second year in the novitiate, there came a deputy from her family with letters urging her immediate return to them.

So short a time remained before she would be of age, yet it was long enough to thwart her at the very end of her tireless effort. Unwilling that this should happen, the nuns approached Bishop St. Vallier. Would he not, they asked, shorten Esther's novitiate, and advance the date of her profession? Once a professed nun, she would be beyond the demands of the secular world. The Bishop agreed.

Spring came to Quebec with a flourish of blue skies and swelling buds and in the convent of the Ursulines the old nuns were heard to say that never had they known a day of such splendor. It was April 12, 1714. In the convent there was an air of bridal festivity. In the great kitchens a feast was being prepared and in the chapel the altar was banked with the freshest flowers and a hundred candles waiting to be lighted.

In an anteroom off the sacristy Esther in her white bridal gown sat with folded hands. The exquisite gown and the veil of priceless lace covering her head were gifts from the de Vaudreuils, sent from Paris. No bride could have been lovelier than this seventeen-year-old girl with her pale, ethereal face and shock of golden curls. The girl, the setting might have been a painting by one of the great masters.

Esther had prayed most of the night, fasting in anticipation of Holy Communion. Now, alone in the antechamber, her black habit, white coif, veil, and rosary on the table beside her, she examined her conscience for perhaps the hundredth time. Had she been right in wounding her parents so? Was she fit to become a nun, to put aside the world and yet serve its wounded in heart and spirit?

She sighed and clasped her cold fingers tighter and for a moment her eyes blurred with tears. Did she perhaps see a little girl in linsey-woolsey and starched pinafore picking blueberries in Wells, Maine? Possibly. Did she catch a glimpse of an Indian camp and an Indian child who whimpered, "Esther, come back?" Did she, briefly, hear the stately measure of the minuet and feel Philippe de Vaudreuil's hand over hers? Then the door opened, admitting Father Bigot, the Mother Superior and a group of the Sisters. In the dis-

tance music swelled into triumphant beauty and high in the belfry she heard the ringing of the bells.

"Come, my child, it is time now." Father Bigot took her hand; the Reverend Mother made the sign of the cross on her brow and lightly kissed her. Someone laid a sheaf of white flowers in her arms. Then she was walking toward a blaze of light and the congregation, its numbers swelled by the highest dignitaries in Quebec, was rising. She heard Father Bigot's voice and her own responses, and presently she was returning to the sacristy. There the bridal gown was laid aside and replaced by the habit and coif of the Ursulines.

Again, and now alone, her heart singing with joy, she approached the altar and prostrated herself. Father Bigot raised her and to the singing of the *Te Deum* he gave her his blessing, and received her as a daughter of the Church. The name Esther Wheelwright had been replaced by Sister Esther Marie Joseph of the Infant Jesus. Serenely, joyously she turned away from all earthly pleasures except as endless duty became pleasure.

All her life through Esther had the joy of an absolutely clear conscience. She had followed God's bidding in the face of discouragement and family disapproval. But the years had brought many affectionate letters from her parents and shortly after her profession the gift of a miniature of her mother, a silver place setting and a silver goblet. In 1754 a nephew came to call on her from Boston and he, too, brought gifts.

94

In the long years that followed no hands were so deft at nursing the sick as Sister Esther Marie Joseph's, no lessons so painlessly learned by restless children as those she taught with such loving patience.

France and Great Britain resumed their war for the possession of the colonies in North America for many years despite treaties and talk of peace. Finally a decisive battle was fought on the Plains of Abraham, a sprawling field outside the city of Quebec, in 1759. It was a hideous battle, one of the bloodiest in North American history. The convent was turned into a hospital and the Sisters were ordered to leave. However, Esther, with seven Sisters to help her, stayed on and cared for the wounded.

By this time she was an aging woman of sixty-two. Forty-five years had passed since the April morning of her investiture but she had lost none of her desire to serve humanity. Neither she nor any member of her little band faltered in the face of the dreadful agony on the battlefield, and scores of dying men called them blessed.

Between her duties with the injured Esther found time to knit long wool socks for the Highlanders whose knees worried her lest they be cold in the frigid Canadian weather! Truly she loved her enemies. Nor had she forgotten her gift of soft laughter and a sense of humor, and many a homesick soldier forgot his heartache when Sister Esther Marie Joseph stood at his bedside and cheered him with a merry tale about Indian life.

James Wolfe, who led the British against Montcalm in that battle of the Plains of Abraham, was only thirty-two years old; Montcalm was forty-seven. Both men were brilliant leaders and both died as the result of wounds suffered in that battle. The chapel of the convent of the Ursulines was heavily damaged during the cannonading but its altar remained intact. Before it Esther led her little band of nuns in speaking the responses when General Montcalm's body was buried there. When at last the guns were silent, it was Esther who led the other Sisters in the task of rebuilding the chapel.

In December of 1760, when the British were established as supreme heads in Canada, a new Mother Superior was elected for the Ursuline order in Quebec. She was Mother Esther Marie Joseph of the Infant Jesus. She was the first English Mother Superior of the Ursulines to be elected and she served three terms. Toward the end of her life her sight failed and she uncomplainingly gave up her beautiful needlework to mend the clothes of the nuns. She was eighty-five when she died and was buried in the convent garden where she had prayed and meditated so often.

From girlhood she had glimpsed the path, leading ever upward, that she must tread, and she had followed it happily, unswervingly to the end.